So what should you be zapping in _____?

Try It Now!

Wherever you see the interactive icon you'll be able to unlock a fun experience to enjoy on your device. There are nine scattered throughout the Annual and one on the front cover to discover. See if you can find them all.

ZAP NOW!

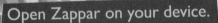

Ready
Open Zappar on your device.

Aim
Scan the code on the page.

Zap
Then point your device at the page and watch it come to life!

To get the best possible experience here are a few hints and tips:

- Connect to wifi if you can and the experiences will download even quicker than on 3G.
- Try and keep the pages as flat as you can for the best effect. Rest the Annual on a table or on the floor.
- Try and keep the full page in view from your phone after scanning the code. Don't get too close or far away if you can help it.

A few helpful tips...

- Try and keep the pages clean and free from tears, pen and other marks as this may affect the experience.
- It's best to view the pages in good lighting conditions if you can.

If you're still having problems then do contact us at support@zappar.com and we'll do our best to help you.

ANGRY BIRDS ™

ROVIO BOOKS

Pedigree®

Published 2014.
Pedigree Books Limited, Beech Hill House, Walnut Gardens, Exeter,
Devon EX4 4DH. www.pedigreebooks.com – books@pedigreegroup.co.uk
The Pedigree trademark, email and website addresses, are the sole
and exclusive properties of PedigreeGroup Limited, used under licence
in this publication.

CONTENTS

UNLOCK BONUS INTERACTIVE FEATURES!

COME AND EGGS-PLORE
PIGGY ISLAND

BIRD
★ ★
APPROVED
★

Welcome to Piggy Island, a land of many wonders and lots of great hiding places. This is the home of the Angry Birds, but it's also where the pigs live – and they'd probably all get along if only King Pig Smooth Cheeks wasn't so keen on eating the birds' eggs!

This year's gone to the birds! Come rain or shine, you can be certain that those greedy pigs will be out there somewhere trying to steal the eggs!

ANGRY TIMES

RED-THE KEY TO THE FLOCK SPEAKS OUT!

(AND WE LISTEN, FROM A DISTANCE AND WEARING A PROTECTIVE HELMET)

WHAT MAKES YOU SEE RED?

Easy one - looking in the mirror! Or a pool of still water, a glass or anything shiny like the back of a spoon...although in the last one

I kind of looked funny and thin, which annoys me!

"DON'T RUFFLE MY FEATHERS!"

NO, WHAT WE MEAN TO ASK IS - WHAT REALLY GETS YOUR GOAT?

My goat? I don't have a goat! It's the eggs I'm worried about!

RIGHT! SO, WHAT MAKES YOU SO ANGRY?

Angry?! Who are you calling angry?!!!? Why that makes me so mad I could just about explode!!!

FACTS FLASH!

RED IS...Serious, protective and dedicated!

LIKES: The eggs! Being in control!

LOATHES: The Pigs and Laziness!

ZAP NOW!

Now, Red is so mad that he's falling apart. Can you help by identifying which part goes where before he completely cracks up?

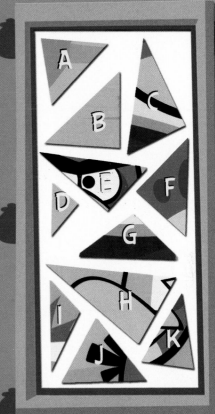

Where do you think the puzzle pieces belong?

1: Puzzle piece ....

2: Puzzle piece ....

3: Puzzle piece ....

4: Puzzle piece ....

5: Puzzle piece ....

6: Puzzle piece ....

SPRING!

It's that wonderful time of year when the days get longer, the weather gets warmer and the birds get angrier!

DESTROY THE PIG FORTRESS!

Can you help the Angry Birds crash through this piggy fortress? Work out the clues to figure out who's best suited to knock down each part of the fortress!

1. Stella can knock down a tower that's one block taller than the one that Bubbles can knock down.

2. Red can knock down the tallest tower.

3. Chuck can knock down a tower that's one block taller than Matilda's, but two blocks shorter than the one Red can destroy.

4. Stella can knock down a tower that's half as tall as the one Matilda can knock down.

5. Bubbles can knock down a tower that's two blocks high.

ZAP NOW!

13

ST PATRICK

St Patrick's Day is upon us, to be sure, and 'tis the time of the year to try your luck at a puzzling game o' chance!

LUCKY SQUARES: Those Angry Birds have got themselves into a fruit punch-up with the pigs! Can you help complete the Sudoku grid for them, ensuring that every line contains only one of each fruit, both up-and-down and left-to-right?

S DAY!

TO BE SURE, TO BE SURE!: These two pictures may look the same at first glance, but they actually feature 8 lucky differences! See if you can find them all-and may the luck o' the Irish be with ye!

VALENTINE'S CARDS

You can cut out, scan or photocopy a card to send to your love! The birds and pigs even wrote some love poems!

You don't yet have wings
You don't yet have legs
But you've captured my heart
You three little eggs!

-Love From Red

Cheep cheepa chirp
Pee-po po
Cheep-chirpa-cheep
Po-po-po!

Translation:
I'm sweet on you,
you're sweet on me
We're the perfect match, so handy!
You're the toffee apple of my eye
I love you, sweet,
sweet candy!

-Love From Bubbles

Roses are red
Violets are blue
Why eat one egg
When I could eat the others too?

-Love From King Pig

You're the fastest chick I know
Going 100 miles per hour
Defending the nest from every foe
And knocking down every pig tower!
There's no question in my heart
You're of superior pedigree
The fastest bird in all the world
Who wouldn't love-me?!

-Love From Chuck

Trying to catch eggs for the king
Often ends with us
all getting beat!
Perhaps he's forgotten
They probably taste rotten
We'd much rather eat
something sweet!

-Love From The Minion pigs

Now it's your turn!

Write a special poem about someone –
or something – you love. It could be
about anything – Angry Birds, a friend,
a pet or even fish fingers!

Good luck!

EASTER EGG HUNT!

It's easter and there are eggs everywhere! And, where there are eggs, there are also pigs - hundreds of them!

Can you find all the silly things hidden in this picture?

You can tick them off as you find them!

1 x broken Easter egg   Easter Egg Terrence

3 x eggs disguised   Stella Easter Bunny
as easter bunnies

A confused Clown pig

8 x pigs disguised   King Pig
as easter bunnies

Jay feeling romantic   An apple

19

ANGRY TIMES

EXCLUSIVE! CHUCK SAYS - DON'T CHUCK ME AWAY!

So, Chuck - what makes your blood boil?

Do you mean if it's a really hot day or when I've done some strenuous flying? Because, let me tell you – I love a hot day and I'm so fit I feel like I could fly forever, man! Blue skies, man, blue skies!

No, we mean what annoys you?

Having so many things to try and not enough time for them all! Like I'd like to go bowling, but also I've been trying to perfect my loop-the-loop trick, and I love painting pictures, and making stuff out of the things I find on the beach, and...wait, I just thought of something new...

"YELLOW IS NEVER SLOW"

Whoa! We get the idea. But, what we really want to know is, what makes you quick to anger?

I'm quick at everything but I'm chilled out. So long as the eggs are safe, everything's best in the nest! Amiright?

20

CHUCK'S FAST CHUCKLES!

What type of bird
follows people around?

A STORKER!

What's an angry
bird's favourite musical
instrument?

THE FLEW-T!

What's the fastest bird
in the world?

A SWIFT!

What's a bird's
favourite martial art?

KUNG-FLEW!

Did you hear about
the angry bird who was
bitten by a vampire?

He became a
FANGry bird!

What do you call a
bird flying backwards?

A DRIB!

How did the bird guess
how big his home was?

HE JUST MADE
A NESTIMATE!

3 STAR
COMEDY!

**FACTS
FLASH!**

CHUCK IS...Competitive,
hyperactive and
easily distracted!

LIKES: Trying new
things!

TOP SECRET

LOATHES:
Thunderstorms!

THE SWINE

KING PIG IN EGG CRACKDOWN!

Today, King Pig Smooth Cheeks announced an island-wide crackdown on eggs. From now on, all eggs must be handed over to King Pig, who promises to take very good care of them.

"As the ruler of Piggy Island, I am taking these steps to ensure the safety of all eggs, be they delicious or yummy," King Pig said in a statement.

SCOFFING!

King Pig was also asked about the persistent complaint that he always eats all the best sweets

and candies. *"As the leader of the pigs, it's my royal duty to test every morsel of food!"* King Pig explained, scoffing rumours of his

scoffing! *"Now, get me those eggs!"*

We wait to see how those feather-brained birds will react to this development.

ZAP NOW!

EXCLUSIVE: THE INSIDE POOP ON THE MINION PIGS!

Today we ask – what the Minion Pigs do to relax?

Minion Pig #1: I love rolling in the mud!

Minion Pig #2: I like to sing – my favourite song is *"Porker Face!"* by Lady Boarboar!

Minion Pig #3: I use an oink pen to write poetry about King Pig.

"We love the king. He's the greatest"

What about your career – where do you see yourself in a year's time?

Minion Pig #1: A long way from here, probably due to a silly mistake with a slingshot! Whee!

Minion Pig #2: Singing for the king – I hope!

Minion Pig #3: I hope to publish a book of all my poetry and call it *"Rhymes for Swines!"*

Why are you all so loyal to King Pig?

Minion Pig #1: Because the king is the best!

Minion Pig #2: Yeah, we love the king. He's the greatest.

Minion Pig #3:
Oh King Pig
You are so big,
Under your crown
You should wear
a pink wig!

Well, there you have it. The minions love their king! It's official!

MUD BATHS ARE REALLY HEALTHY, SAY EXPERTS!

Every pig loves wallowing in the filthy mud! But shocking research reveals that mud baths may actually be quite healthy and could be good for your skin. It sounds like hogwash but this hogwash could change the way hogs wash!

OFF DUTY

Red had been alone guarding the eggs for so long that he was starting to go cuckoo! Matilda insisted that Red take a holiday. But Red wasn't sure – if he wasn't around, who would look after the eggs? "The flock will!" Matilda promised.

Red still wasn't sure. The other birds in the flock spent most of their time goofing off and being silly – could they really be trusted to guard the precious eggs? However, Red did need that holiday – so finally, he agreed to go.

It didn't take long for Red to reach South Beach where he could put his feet up and relax in the sun. But everywhere he looked, he imagined the eggs! There were egg stones, egg drinks – even the sun looked like an egg!

Red realised he had better just get back to the nest – if he stayed away from the eggs any longer he would go even more cuckoo than he had before!

Meanwhile, the other birds were not taking their job of guarding the eggs very seriously at all. Instead, they were being silly – in fact, they all thought that Red worried far too much about the eggs.

But while the birds goofed off, some greedy piggies snuck through the bushes towards the flock. Biding their time, the pigs waited until the birds were distracted and then seized the eggs!

While the rest of the flock were being surprised by the empty nest, Red was making his way home from the other side of the island without a care in the world. His holiday had been a wash out – he'd spent the whole time worrying about the eggs – but he felt relaxed now that he was finally on his way home.

So you can probably imagine Red's reaction when he got home to find the eggs were missing – he was livid! Red should have known better than to trust those other bird brains in the flock! They were all still too dazed to do anything but look very sorry for themselves!

RED'S GONNA BE SOOOOO ANGRY! MAYBE WE SHOULD MAKE HIM SOME ICED TEA!

GULP...

Red searched for the eggs alone, racing to the nearest pig tower and knocking down every pig that stood in his way until he found them. It didn't take long for him to locate the eggs and he brought them back to the nest quicker than you can boil an egg! Which was exactly what King Pig had been planning!

When he got back to the nest, Red's friends told him that they were very sorry. They should have been paying more attention to the eggs. Red was about to tell them off...but he couldn't. After everything that had happened today, Red realised that they all needed a holiday!

WE'RE SORRY!

Red took the whole flock to South Beach where they could all relax in the sun. But Red kept the best deck chairs for his three favourites – the eggs! Red had learnt a valuable lesson that day – everyone needs a holiday once in a while! Otherwise, they get tired and end up with egg on their face!

THE END

SUMMER!

LONG DAYS OUT WITH PLENTY OF ICE CREAM TO KEEP COOL! BUT, WHEN THE TEMPERATURE'S RISING, TEMPERS GROW SHORT – AND THE ANGRY BIRDS GET REALLY, REALLY ANGRY!

You can warm up your brain cells with this summer crossword!

ACROSS

1. It's next to the sea. (5 letters)

3. In summer the ____ are warmer! (4 letters)

5. The season after Spring. (6 letters)

DOWN

1. Jim, Jake and Jay are known as this. (5 letters)

2. When pigs are around, the birds should keep their eggs ____ (6 letters)

4. Beaches are often this! (5 letters)

LONG SUMMER DAYS!

FUN IN THE SUN!

YOU WILL NEED:

A blank sheet of paper or something else to cover up this page.

A clock or timer.

INSTRUCTIONS: Set your timer and study the image for one minute. Try to remember everything you can about the image (you could even try saying things that you see out loud). Once the minute is over, cover the image and then answer the questions on the opposite page.

1. Who is wearing sunglasses?

....

2. Is Bubbles eating an ice cream or an ice lolly?

....

3. How many birds are wearing hats?

....

4. What colour flower does Stella wear in her hair?

....

5. *True or false* Matilda is playing a trumpet.

....

6. How many Blue Birds are next to the glass of punch?

....

7. Name five fruits seen in the image.

....

8. Who is guarding an egg?

....

9. *True or false* Chuck is wearing a hula skirt.

....

10. Which bird is standing next to Stella?

....

11. How many bananas can you see
        in the image?

....

ZAP NOW!

SOARING MIGHTY EAGLE

NOW'S YOUR CHANCE TO MAKE A MIGHTY EAGLE PAPER PLANE!

YOU WILL NEED:

- A Sheet of A4 paper with a scan or photocopy of the opposite page.

- If you can't copy the page, you can carefully tear it out, or you can just use a blank sheet of paper and draw your own eagle design on it. Drawing's cool!

REMEMBER:
Never launch your eagle at a person's face or at a pet.

1. Crease the paper down the centre along its longest line (With your eagle markings facing down).

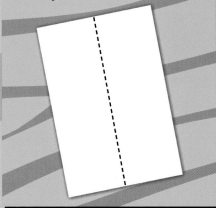

2. Now fold in the top corners so that they meet the middle crease in two roughly equilateral triangles.

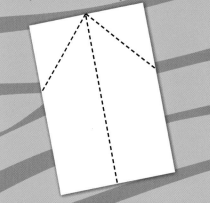

3. Make a longer, narrower triangle that goes roughly three-quarters of the length of the paper. Do this for both sides.

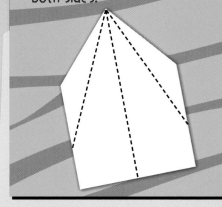

Mighty Eagle is the most mysterious of the Angry Birds. Rumour has it that he was once the mightiest warrior in the flock... but that was a very long time ago! Now he keeps to himself and only gets involved with the other birds when things are at their worst for the flock and their eggs. What an old grumpy bird!

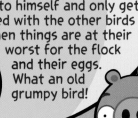

4. Fold the two sides together down the centre crease that you first made, closing it like a book.

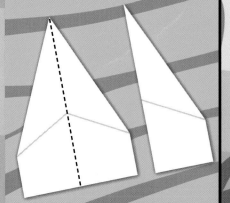

5. Now, turn the sheet until the centre line is facing you. Then fold down the side so that it is roughly half the height. Repeat for both sides.

TOP TIPS TO MAKE THE PLANE FLY:

1. Hold it by the undercarriage (the centre line you first created) with the nose pointing forwards, then throw it like a dart.

2. If you hold it in the middle and throw it slowly the eagle will glide further. Hold it by the nose to make it go faster!

3. If you want to make it even faster, add more weight to the nose using stickers, sticky tape or by clipping a paperclip to the front.

Take to the Skies

A Cool Summer Story!

Can you help with this story? We've given you the start and the end – but you'll need to make up the rest and draw it in the panels.

One day, the birds were relaxing at the beach. But they didn't notice some stinky pigs had also gone to the beach...

I'm going to paddle in the sea!

Me too!

Me three!

The eggs were safe at last!

From now on the only hot water I want to get in...

is the sea!

The ever-egging end.

WASHED UP!

HERE'S A SUPER STRATEGY GAME FOR TWO!

YOU WILL NEED:

A friend

Two playing tokens (which you can cut out from this page)

A die.

THE GAME:

A great storm has washed up lots of strange objects on South Beach. Some of these objects are useful while some are nothing but trouble!

The aim of the game is to travel across the beach from left to right.

The first player to reach the safe zone is the winner.

HOW TO PLAY:

Each player chooses a token and places it on one of the starting squares at the left of the beach.

Roll the dice to see who goes first.

Players must move towards the right at all times, moving either in a straight line, diagonally or in any combination of both – so long as they always move towards the right.

When a player lands on a square featuring an object, they must follow the instructions listed in the key on this page.

IMPORTANT: Every time a player rolls the dice, they may either move their piece or their opponent's piece that number of squares! However, if a player moves their opponent's piece, they must still move it to the right – no trying to move them backwards, and no trying to split the move between you and them!

Sometimes a player will have to decide if it's better to move their opponent forward or land on something bad themselves!

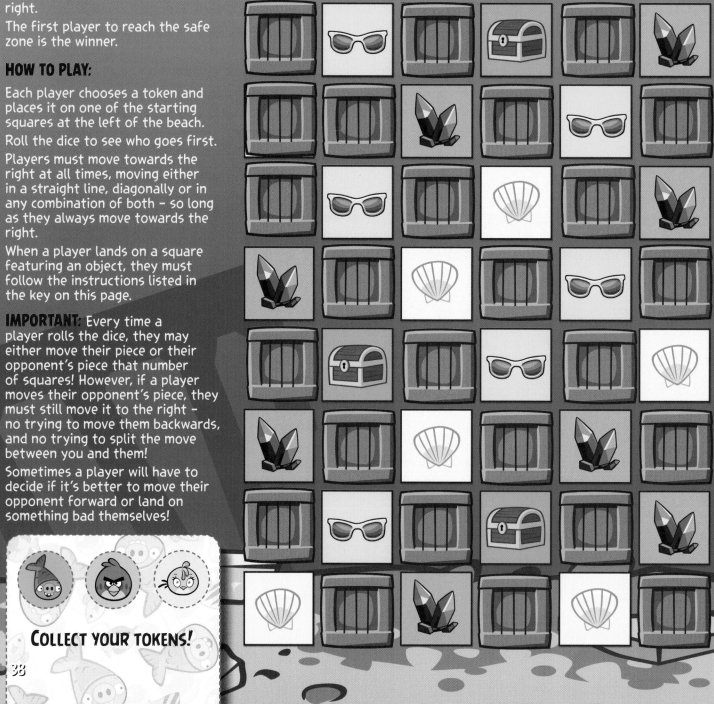

COLLECT YOUR TOKENS!

HERE IS YOUR SQUARE KEY!

 REST...

 MOVE FORWARD TWO SQUARES.

 MOVE BACK THREE SQUARES.

 THROW AGAIN!

 MOVE YOUR OPPONENT BACK TWO!

 DOUBLE YOUR NEXT DICE THROW.

 SAFE BEACH!

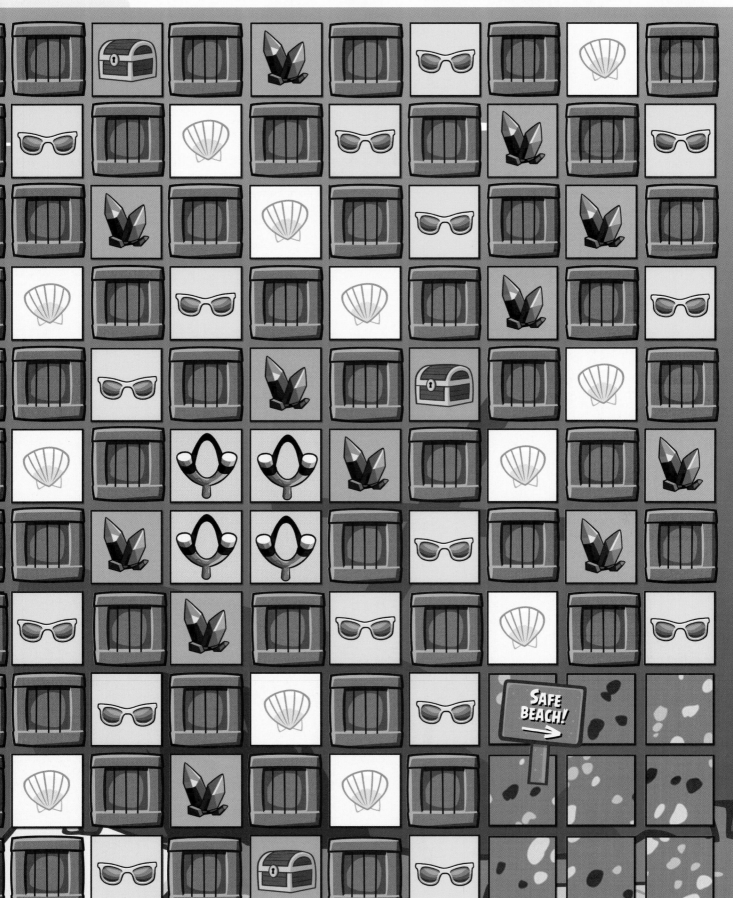

ANGRY TIMES

EXCLUSIVE: WE EGG MATILDA ON!

So, MATILDA-WHAT RUFFLES YOUR FEATHERS?

Any strong breeze!

No, WHAT WE MEAN TO ASK IS-WHAT IRRITATES YOU?

When my flower arrangements get blown about by the wind. Coo, that can be really annoying after spending all morning trying to get them looking nice!

WHAT WE REALLY WANT TO KNOW IS WHAT MAKES YOU ANGRY?

I am never angry. I am always a picture of calm.

And if you look at my plants like that again I will peck you into next week, buddy! Don't think I didn't see you!!!

"DROP IT LIKE IT'S HOT!"

FLOWER MAZE!

Yipes! Matilda's garden has become so overgrown it's becoming hard to find her way around. Can you help her navigate a route that takes her to her meditation pond without running into anyone...friends OR fowl...?

FACTS FLASH!

MATILDA IS: Caring, sensitive and optimistic!

LIKES: Gardening! Fussing over others!

LOATHES: Anyone fussing over her!

THE SWINE

EXCLUSIVE: FOREMAN PIG DISHES THE DIRT!

What is your greatest quality?

Foreman Pig: My good looks! Or maybe my brains! I'd say it's my good-looking brain! No wait, my brainy good looks!

If you're so smart, how come your plans always go wrong?

Foreman Pig: Well, that depends on how you define "wrong".

Your towers always collapse, risking the lives of your minions and you never capture the eggs!

Foreman Pig: Hey! Maybe I mean to have my towers collapse, risking Minion Pigs' lives and never capturing the eggs! Did you ever think of that, smart guy?

PIGS MAKE SMELLY MESS, SURPRISING NO ONE!

Once again, Minion Pigs have managed to make a sow's ear out of a silk purse when...

cont on page 7

FOREMAN PIG'S SOGGY PUZZLE

Can you believe that one of Foreman Pig's plans has actually been successful? Not only has he caught an egg, he's also captured an unconscious Angry Bird and still has one loyal Minion Pig left to help him get back to Pig City before the other birds catch up with him!

But there's a problem! Foreman Pig has a fast-flowing river to cross and the rowing boat he's built can only hold two things – himself and one of the things he's taking back to Pig City.

Of course, being a greedy pig, Foreman Pig wants to take everything back with him so he figures out that he'll have to make several trips across the river taking each item in turn.

But there's a catch – if he leaves the Minion Pig alone with the egg he suspects that the Pig will eat it! But if he leaves the Angry Bird with the Minion Pig, the Bird could wake up and push the pig into the river before escaping and calling for help! The Angry Bird would never hurt the egg, of course! How can Foreman Pig get everything across the river safely?

YOU CAN FILL IN YOUR ANSWER HERE!

This is the answer!
(don't look until you're ready!)

Foreman Pig must first take the Minion Pig across to the other bank and leave him there. Next he returns and takes either the egg or the Angry Bird across to the other side. Because he cannot leave the Minion Pig with either the egg or the Angry Bird, he then returns to the other bank with the Minion Pig in his boat. He leaves the Minion Pig on the bank and collects whatever he left behind there - the egg or the Angry Bird–which he takes across to the other side. Now the egg and the Angry Bird are on the far side. Minion Pig returns one last time to pick up the Minion Pig before rowing once more across the river to the far bank...where he finds a whole flock of Angry Birds waiting for him having awoken their friend and taken their egg back. Bad luck, Foreman Pig!

43

CODE CRACKLING!

These pigs look as if they're lined up for pigrobics in the park, but in fact they're arranged in a special code.

Can you crack the code and work out the secret message?

What is a witch's best school subject?
SPELLING!

What do you get if you cross a pig with an angry bird?

a. Swine Flew!
b. A pig in a flap!
c. Muddy feathers!

Why are pigs no fun?

a. Because they're BOARing!
b. Because they're TROUGH to be around!
c. Because they always Pignore you!

How do you recognise a fashionable pig?

a. He wears what's in STYle!
b. He knows what's in and what's SNOUT!
c. Because he always looks MUDern!

How does a pig story book begin?

a. With the BACONtents!
b. "Oinks upon a time..."
c. I don't know, but it's bound to end with a curly tale!

What's a pig's favourite game?

a. Swinecraft!
b. Snorts and crosses!
c. Trivial Pigsuit!

What's a pig's favourite film?

a. Despigable Me!
b. Harry Trotter and the Hoglet of Fire!
c. Star Boars!

EASY A!

SQUAWK!

WORD SEARCH

```
A E G C H T S E N I J G F K L V
M B A N O D P G Q R G S W P T H
I G J N F P A E M E W B C O O M
U E L M G R H F Y J N D P A S I
F D F C S R O I M B R G W C J P
L K G N P E Y Y F J L H O H Q R
I I A O T W P E K D N I C M L F
G C R H J O G M F W K O S D P N
H P B M L T Y N I J S G R U E K
T V E N G O C L H B M A O I P S
Y F O I D K P E S W Z N C R G U
R H J A N G Q Y K F O O I M P O
M B O F E A T H E R S R O C F I
L P S M G E U I O J H K L M N R
Q A R K N C T F P B M G I D O U
I S L I N G S H O T N E M K B F
```

Class is in session! Can you find all these words or will you end up in detention?

EGG ☐ FLIGHT ☐

ANGRY ☐ ZOOM ☐

FURIOUS ☐ NEST ☐

FEATHERS ☐ SLINGSHOT ☐

POACH ☐ TOWER ☐

ARISE... FRANKENSWINE!

IT'S THE NIGHT OF THE LIVING PORK AND FOREMAN PIG AND CHEF PIG HAVE COMBINED THEIR DARK ARTS TO COOK UP A MONSTER PIG THAT THEY HOPE WILL BE ABLE STAND UP TO THE ANGRY BIRDS AND STEAL THEIR EGGS.

FRANKENSWINE THE FIRST

I cooked him up but he's put on too much weight!

Their first monstrous attempt was to create a towering pig, one who could overpower the Angry Birds with his height. But this towering monster proved too unstable – and kept eating the yummy 'glue' that joined him together!

Their second Frankenswine took parts of Foreman Pig's weirdest machines and combined them with dozy pigs to create a pig-cyborg that could crush eggs to dust. Of course, crushing eggs is the last thing they needed it to do. Oops!

FRANKENSWINE THE SECOND

Oh well, back to the drawing board!

48

NOW IT'S YOUR TURN! USE ALL YOUR DRAWING SKILLS TO CREATE THE ULTIMATE PIG MONSTER. JUST REMEMBER A FRANKENSWINE TAKES NO PRISONERS AND HAS NO MERCY!

IT'S BRILLIANT! WE'RE SAVED!

HALLOWE'EN MAKE-IT MASKS

YOU COULD CUT YOUR MASK OUT OR SCAN IT IN AND RESIZE IT! THE CHOICE IS YOURS!

ASK AN ADULT FOR HELP WITH SCISSORS!

PIG or TREAT

LET'S SMASH SOME PUMPKINS

YOU WILL NEED:

1. Thin elastic, string or wool.
2. Scissors (ask a grown-up to help).
3. Sticky tape.
4. Glue.
5. Thin cardboard.

INSTRUCTIONS:

1. Choose one of the masks and stick the mask design to the cardboard – you can either be an angry bird or a greedy pig!

2. Once the glue has dried, cut around the mask and cardboard.

3. Use the scissors to score holes for the eyes. A good tip is to place the eyes of the mask onto a lump of Blu-tack or plasticine – this way you can push through without tearing the mask or damaging anything else!

4. Cut enough elastic/wool/string to fit around the back of your head.

5. Attach the elastic/wool/string to the back of the mask with some sticky tape.

6. Go out and scare everyone with your new Hallowe'en look!

51

Hallowe'en is the time for scary stories. Here's one of the scariest! It's called...

KING PIGS
GREEDY SURPRISE!

King Pig was having the most delicious day. His chef had created an artificial egg that he promised would taste just like the real thing.

"I can't wait to try it," King Pig squealed, licking his lips.

So, chef Pig gave the King a large spoon and told him to get cracking.

King Pig swung his spoon down on the egg, breaking its shell and releasing the gooey yolk inside. With a slurp, greedy King Pig ate the whole thing! It was delicious!

"More!" he demanded greedily.

Chef Pig brought a second egg to the royal table, which King Pig ate in a flash. then he brought another and another and another, and each one was cracked open and scoffed by the greedy king.

With each egg he ate, King Pig became larger and rounder until before very long he looked rather like an egg himself!

"If you eat any more eggs you will surely explode," chef Pig insisted.

But King Pig wouldn't hear of it! He just kept eating more and more eggs, enough to feed a hundred hungry piggies.

Eventually, King Pig's appetite began to slow down – but he was still greedy enough to want to eat another egg. Rolling his now-ginormous body, King Pig insisted on one more egg. chef Pig obliged, bringing another egg out from his kitchen and placing

it in the egg cup before the king.

But King Pig was too fat to move now, and he could only stare at the egg.

It was then that the egg began to speak! "Well, if you're not going to eat me," it said in a decidedly eggy voice, "I'll have to eat you!"

King Pig screamed in fear as the egg produced a giant spoon, ready to eat him!

But as the spoon swung towards his crown, King woke up-he must have fallen asleep! So, it had all been a nightmare, no doubt brought on by eating all those eggs!

"In future, I'll just eat a few eggs at a time," King Pig decided, rubbing his sore belly. But chef Pig had bad news. "I'm afraid we're all out of ingredients," he explained. "I can't make any more eggs!"

King Pig screamed even louder at that then when he'd thought the egg was going to eat him!

THE END

Now it's your turn – can you think of a scary story starring the Angry Birds? We've started you off:

IT WAS A DARK AND STORMY NIGHT ON PIGGY ISLAND. RED WAS GUARDING THE NEST WHEN HE HEARD A STRANGE NOISE COMING FROM VERY CLOSE BY. "WHAT WAS THAT?" RED WONDERED...

ANGRY TIMES

EXCLUSIVE: WE ASK - WHAT SETS BOMB OFF?

WHAT MAKES YOU STRESSED?

Dressed? That's a funny question because I almost never wear clothes...except maybe a hat and some shades when it's sunny.

NOT DRESSED - WHAT MAKES YOU STRESSED?

Oh, rest! Yes, I love a good sleep.

NO, STRESSED - NOT REST!

What's that? Look, I blew up earlier today and my hearing's not come back properly yet. You will have to speak up.

Hey, calm down, buddy - you seem kind of...what's the word I'm looking for?

STRESSED?

What? No, not that. It'll come to me... stressed! That's it. You seem stressed.

AAARRR HHHH HH!

WHAT MAKES YOU STRESSED? STRESSED! S-T-R-E-S-S-E-D!!!

FACTS FLASH!

BOMB IS...Popular, explosive and Silly!

LIKES: Blowing stuff up!

LOATHES: Chores! Being rushed!

EXCLUSIVE: STELLA AND THE BLUES INTERVIEW – THESE BIRDS ARE FLIGHTY!

STELLA – WHAT'S IT LIKE BEING THE CUTEST BIRD IN THE FLOCK?

Stella: Me? Cute? You've got the wrong chick, pal – I'm a can-do bird who kicks tail feathers!

Blues: Yeah, we're waaaaay cuter than Stella! Look at us – we're small, we're cheeky! And there's three of us!

WELLLLLL, YOU BLUES ARE AWFULLY CUTE TOO...

Stella: Yup, they're the cute ones all right! I'm just here to chew bubble gum and kick pig tail...and I'm all out of bubble gum!

Blues: We can kick pig tail too, you know! Three times as fast as Stella – because there's three of us! Jim, Jake and Jay always rule the day!

GUYS – THIS IS NOT A COMPETITION!

Stella: Exactly! That's what I've been trying to tell them!

Blues: Okay, we're happy to come in second place...and third and first! Hah-hah! Hah-hah! Hah-hah!

SLINGSHOT 101

One day, as Red was guarding the eggs, he heard a lot of noise coming from the slingshot. When he went to see what was causing the commotion he found the three Blues – Jim, Jake and Jay – riding atop the slingshot on their skateboards!

Red was so angry he could hardly chirp. He told the Blues to stop larking around and that the slingshot should never be used as a toy! It was far too dangerous!

The Blues didn't care. Before long they were back bouncing on the slingshot and using it like a swing. So Red came over to tell them off again. This time, he decided to show them just how dangerous the slingshot could be by climbing in it.

The Blues watched silently as Red drew back the slingshot and prepared to launch. At that moment, Red spotted a search party of pigs sneaking up on the nest – where he had left the eggs unguarded!

But before Red could alert the others, the slingshot fired and he was launched high into the sky!

Red landed on a distant mountain with a crash! Now he was a very long way from the nest.

Red couldn't help but imagine what had happened to the eggs and the Blues while he hurried back to the nest. He imagined the Blues had been overwhelmed and the eggs were about to be eaten by King Pig himself!

Red ran as fast as he could back to the nest, expecting the very worst! But, when he arrived, do you know what he saw? The eggs were fine, and the naughty piggies were confused and bedazzled because of the tricks the Blues had played on them.

Red was very proud of the Blues as they fired the pigs high into the sky. Those pesky pigs wouldn't be coming back anytime soon!

After that, Red was a lot more relaxed about what the Blues did around the slingshot. In fact, he even joined them skateboarding from its curves! Skateboarding, Red realised, was wheely good fun!

THE END

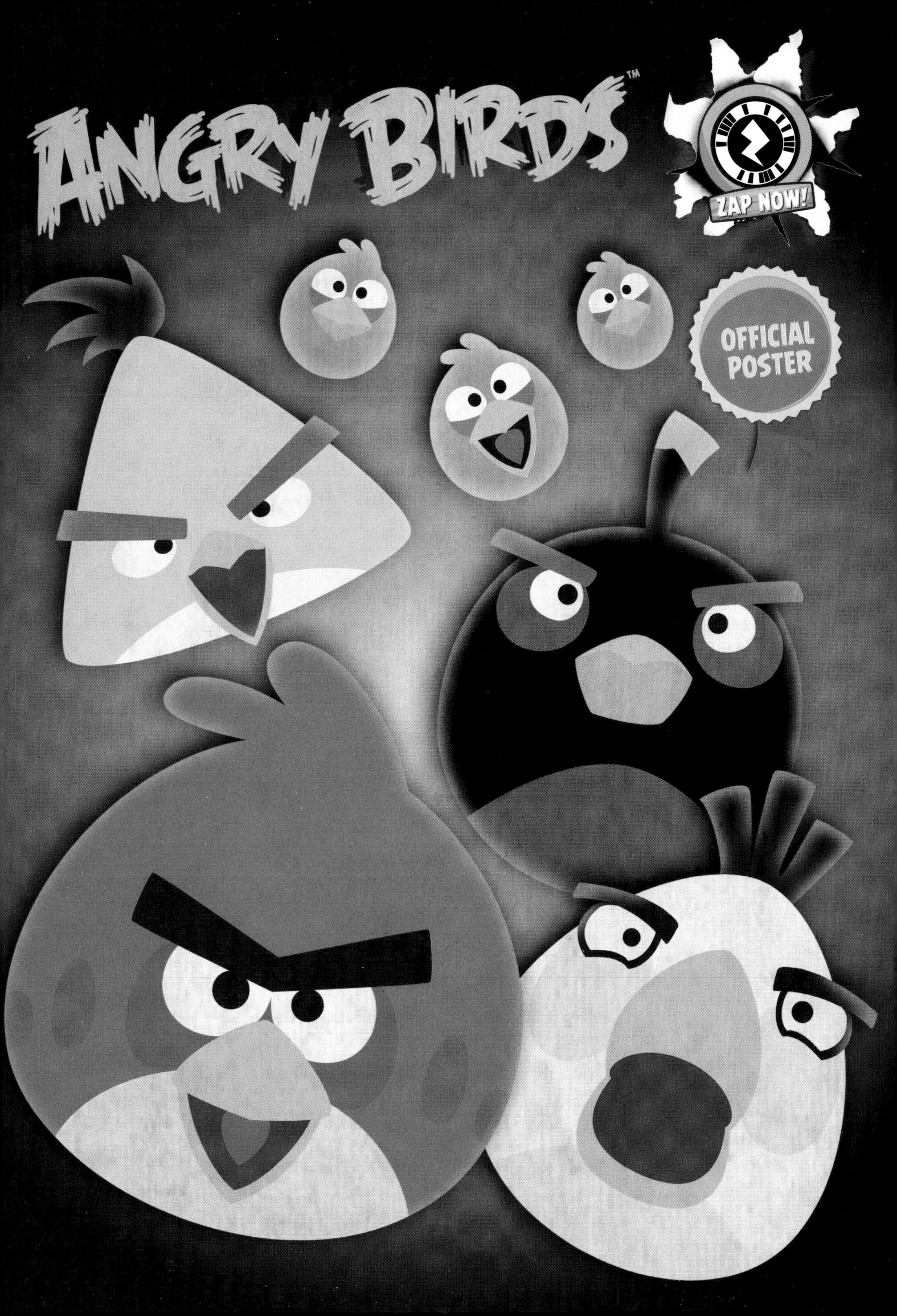

ANGRY BIRDS™
ZAP NOW!
OFFICIAL POSTER

WINTER!

SNOW AND ICE AND ALL THINGS COLD! IT SEEMS SOMETIMES THE ONLY THING KEEPING THE BIRDS WARM IS HAVING THEIR BLOOD BOIL WITH ANGER!

What type of bird is always out of breath?

A PUFFIN!

Winter means Christmas and Christmas means presents!
Can you count up how many of each colour present the Angry
Birds gave to their buddies?

The Angry Birds gave......................presents.

 X .... X ....

 X .... X ....

What else is hidden among the
presents? How many are there?

....

Make the World's Angriest CHRISTMAS CARDS!

YOU WILL NEED:

1. Scan or photocopy the opposite page.

2. A piece of A4 card folded to create A5 size.

3. Paper glue.

4. Scissors (ask an adult to help).

5. A pen or pencil.

6. A soaring imagination!

INSTRUCTIONS:

1. First glue the design to some card. Remember to place it facing you on the right hand side of the fold.

2. Add some words inside. Maybe "Merry Eggs-mas!" or "Have a beak-tastic Christmas!"

3. That's it – you're done! Now you just need someone to give the card to!

TOP TIP:

You could dress up your card by adding some glitter or shiny stickers of your own!

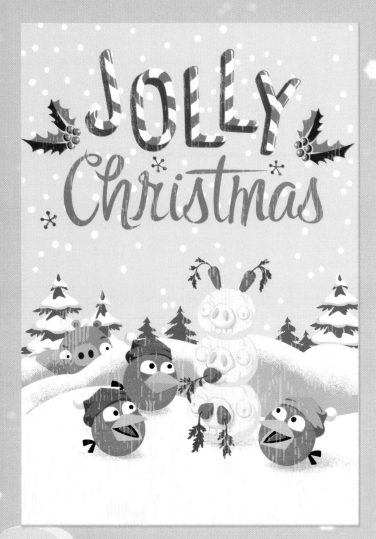

CHRISTMAS FUN!

CHRISTMAS COOKIE CHAOS!

Can you help King Pig find his way through this Christmas Cookie Maze to his delicious glass of milk? Without running into any birds!

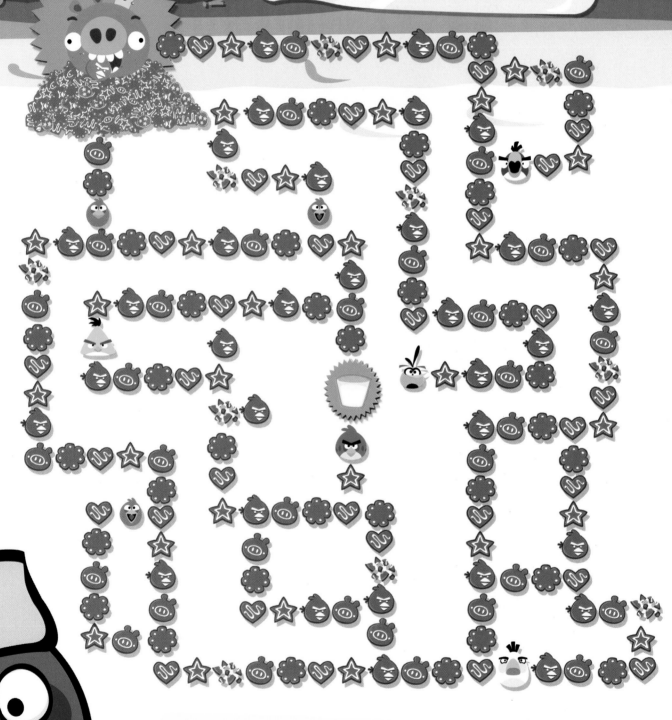

Where did the pig go to visit Father Christmas?
SANTA'S TROTTO!

Why did the teacher take a register of the Christmas gifts?

TO MAKE SURE EVERYONE WAS PRESENT!

ZAP NOW!

HO HO...HO-NO!

SEASON'S GREEDINGS!

Can you spot all eight differences between these Christmas cards?

SEASONS GREEDINGS!

Knock Over The Pig*

CHRISTMAS TREES!

This slingshot launches the birds different distances depending on how heavy they are. Can you work out which bird should be launched at which tree from the facts below? Remember – each bird only has time to launch once!

1. Red can glide 25 BMUs further than Matilda.

2. Bomb is too heavy for the slingshot and can only reach half the distance that Matilda can reach.

3. Stella is much lighter than average and can be thrown three times as far as Bomb can.

4. If he gets a good run up, speedy Chuck can go over twice as far as Matilda.

5. Matilda can be launched 30 BMUs.

*BMU = BIRD MEASUREMENT UNIT

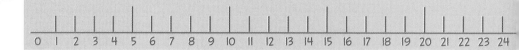

0 1 2 3 4 5 6 7 8 9 10 11 12 13 14 15 16 17 18 19 20 21 22 23 24

CAN YOU FIGURE OUT WHICH BIRD CAN KNOCK DOWN WHICH TREE?

A..

B..

C..

D..

E..

WINTER BLUNDERLAND!

Snow has hit Piggy Island, hiding
everything under a crisp, white coat!
But those greedy pigs have seized their
chance to steal the eggs under the cover
of the snow.

Can you find the eggs – and all the other things on the list hidden by all of the snow?

Eggs in nest ◯

Christmas Hat Red ◯

Icy Foreman Pig ◯

4 x Reindeer Pigs ◯

3 x Snowpigs ◯

Bewildered Miner Pig ◯

Snorkel Pig ◯

3 x rotten pumpkins left over from Hallowe'en ◯

RED has his own speed boost to hang onto pole position!

Watch out for **BOMB!** He can blow up nearby racers!

THE BLUES can use 3 x mini speed boosts to get ahead!

CHUCK has a mega speed boost to race ahead of the competition!

MATILDA throws egg bombs at other racers to slow them down! *Icky!*

TERENCE creates destructive storms that can rock other drivers off course!

STELLA can generate a protective bubble around herself!

BUBBLES expands to super size to grab all the bonuses!

HAL is able to create a tornado to slow down other racers!

KING PIG uses crafty balloons to fly over the race track and out of danger!

FOREMAN PIG is armed with 3 x TNT dynamite that he throws at his opponents!

CORPORAL PIG protects himself from other drivers with his helmet shield!

SNOUTRUN GAME!

Think you have what it takes to outrun the pigs on the track? Now's your chance to prove it in this feather - raising race for the pole position perch!

YOU WILL NEED:

- 2-4 players.
- Counters (you may cut out the counters from this page, or make your own).
- A dice.

HOW TO PLAY:

1. Each player chooses a car and places it on the starting grid.
2. Roll to see who starts – highest goes first (roll again if two people get the same!).
3. Each player makes their way around the track, following the instructions on each square.
4. The winner is the one who reaches the finish line first! Simple!

START

2
Stalled car - go back to starting grid for your next turn.

3
Lost in the exhaust - miss a go!

14
Last place loser - if you're in last place, roll again!

15
Speed boost – roll again!

16
Out of fuel - miss a go while you refuel!

17
Tyre damage slows you down - you must roll a 2 or 3 to leave or stay and try again!

18

19
Fuel running low - roll the dice twice and take the lowest number for your go!

20
Avoid rough ground - take short cut

GO TO 23

21
Last place loser - if you're in last place, roll again!

GO TO 23

RED

THE BLUES

KING PIG

CORPORAL PIG

COLLECT YOUR TOKENS!

4

5
Great start!
Roll again!

6

GO TO 6

7

GO TO 5
8
Slip on
oil slick,
go back.

9

13
Fuel injection!
Double your
next roll!

GO TO 14

12
Clear road
bonus – if you're
first you may
roll again!

GO TO 14

11
Super slick
gear change –
accelerate

GO TO 14

10
Take a corner
too sharply
and spin out!

GO TO 9

22
Slipped in the
mud. On your
next go, you can
only move if you
roll a 6.

GO TO 23

PIT STOP

24
Clashing gears!
Roll again,
but you
must go
backwards!

GO TO 23

GO TO 23

25
Cheat with
this shortcut.
But remember –
cheaters never
prosper!

GO TO 29

26
Spin out! Miss
your next turn
unless you
throw a 1!

GO TO 29

GO TO 23

27

GO TO 29

GO TO 29

FINISH

29

28
Engine
overheats
– go back via
the pits.

GO TO 29

GO TO 29

GO TO 29

PIG SNORTS

How do pigs greet each other?
They sty five!

How do pigs celebrate the
New Year?
With a hog-mannay party!

How did the pigs surprise
the angry birds?
They set up a hambush!

How do spy pigs communicate?
They use invisible oink!

What's a pig's
favourite magazine?
The pig issue!

What type of games do pigs
like best?
Board games!

Did you hear
about the pigs
who caught
a cold?
**Doctors said
it was a
snoutbreak!**

How do you recognise
a well-dressed pig?
**He's the one wearing
a bow sty!**

Did you hear about the baby
pig who mixed up all his toys
in the bath?
They came out in a muddle!

What day of the week does
a pig start school?
Gammonday!

How do you get a pig to work
for you?
**Get him to sign a
bacontract!**

And how does the pig know he
has the job?
**He's told he's been
app-oink-ted!**

ANSWERS

PAGE 9
I=B, 2=H, 3=J, 4=E, 5=C, 6G

PAGE 12-13
1. Matilda - 6 blocks
2. Stella - 3 blocks.
3. Chuck - 7 blocks.
4. Bubbles - 2 blocks.
5. Red - 9 blocks.

PAGE 14
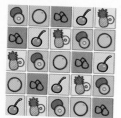

PAGE 15

PAGE 18-19

PAGE 31

PAGE 32-33
1. Bomb, 2. Ice Lolly, 3. 2,
4. Pink, 5. False, 6. 2, 7.
Grapes, Kiwi, Pineapple,
Star Fruit, Mango,
Banana, Melon, Orange,
Papaya 8. Terence, 9.
False, 10. Matilda, 11. 2

PAGE 41

PAGE 45
Good Oink! This is a very important message to tell you that the pig circus will be visiting next weekend. There will be clown pigs, juggling pigs and acrobatic pigs! Attendance is mandatory. Have fun or I will be very, very cross!
Hogs and kisses,
King Pig

PAGE 47

PAGE 63
10 Red Presents, 9 Green Presents, 9 Blue Presents, 10 Yellow Presents, and 3 Golden Eggs

PAGE 66

PAGE 67

SEASONS GREEDINGS!

PAGE 68-89
A. Bomb, B. Matilda,
C. Stella, D. Red, E. Chuck

PAGE 70-71

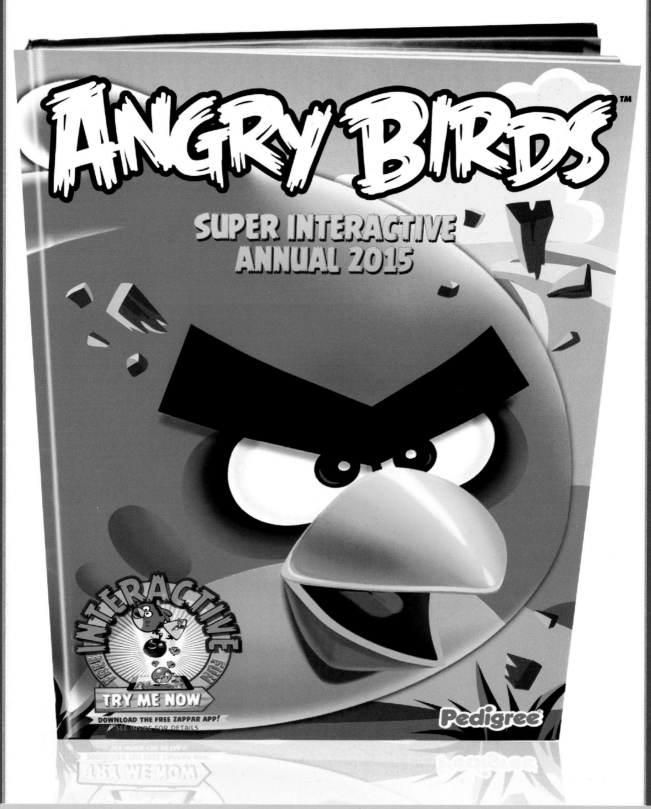